ONE DIRECTION

WISE PUBLICATIONS
PART OF THE MUSIC SALES GROUP
LONDON / NEW YORK / PARIS / SYDNEY / COPENHAGEN / BERLIN / MADRID / HONG KONG / TOKYO

ALSO AVAILABLE IN THE REALLY EASY PIANO SERIES...

ABBA
25 GREAT HITS. ORDER NO. AM980430

CHILDREN'S FAVOURITES
20 POPULAR HITS. ORDER NO. AM998745

CHRISTMAS
24 FESTIVE CHART HITS. ORDER NO. AM980496

CLASSICAL FAVOURITES
24 WELL-KNOWN FAVOURITES. ORDER NO. AM993366

COLDPLAY
20 SONGS FROM COLDPLAY. ORDER NO. AM989593

ELTON JOHN
24 CLASSIC SONGS. ORDER NO. AM987844

FRANK SINATRA
21 CLASSIC SONGS. ORDER NO. AM987833

GREAT FILM SONGS
22 BIG FILM HITS. ORDER NO. AM993344

GREAT SHOWSTOPPERS
20 POPULAR STAGE SONGS. ORDER NO. AM993355

JAZZ GREATS
22 JAZZ FAVOURITES. ORDER NO. AM1000857

LOVE SONGS
22 CLASSIC LOVE SONGS. ORDER NO. AM989582

MICHAEL JACKSON
19 CLASSIC HITS. ORDER NO. AM1000604

MORE 21ST CENTURY HITS
21 POPULAR HITS. ORDER NO. AM996534

MOZART
22 CLASSICAL FAVOURITES. ORDER NO. AM1000648

NEW CHART HITS
19 BIG CHART HITS. ORDER NO. AM996523

NO. 1 HITS
22 POPULAR CLASSICS. ORDER NO. AM993388

POP HITS
22 GREAT SONGS. ORDER NO. AM980408

SHOWSTOPPERS
24 STAGE HITS. ORDER NO. AM982784

TV HITS
25 POPULAR HITS. ORDER NO. AM985435

60S HITS
25 CLASSIC HITS. ORDER NO. AM985402

70S HITS
25 CLASSIC SONGS. ORDER NO. AM985413

80S HITS
25 POPULAR HITS. ORDER NO. AM985424

90S HITS
24 POPULAR HITS. ORDER NO. AM987811

50 FABULOUS SONGS
FROM POP SONGS TO CLASSICAL THEMES. ORDER NO. AM999449

50 GREAT SONGS
FROM POP SONGS TO CLASSICAL THEMES. ORDER NO. AM995643

50 HIT SONGS
FROM POP HITS TO JAZZ CLASSICS. ORDER NO. AM1000615

PIANO TUTOR
FROM FIRST STEPS TO PLAYING IN A WIDE
RANGE OF STYLES — FAST!. ORDER NO. AM996303

ALL TITLES CONTAIN BACKGROUND NOTES FOR EACH SONG PLUS
PLAYING TIPS AND HINTS.

PUBLISHED BY
WISE PUBLICATIONS
14-15 BERNERS STREET, LONDON, W1T 3LJ, UK.

EXCLUSIVE DISTRIBUTORS:
MUSIC SALES LIMITED
DISTRIBUTION CENTRE, NEWMARKET ROAD, BURY ST EDMUNDS,
SUFFOLK, IP33 3YB, UK.
MUSIC SALES PTY LIMITED
UNITS 3-4, 17 WILLFOX STREET, CONDELL PARK
NSW 2200, AUSTRALIA.

ORDER NO. AM1006632
ISBN 978-1-78305-125-0
THIS BOOK © COPYRIGHT 2013 BY WISE PUBLICATIONS,
A DIVISION OF MUSIC SALES LIMITED.

MUSIC ARRANGED BY FIONA BOLTON.
EDITED BY JENNI NOREY.
PRINTED IN THE EU.

YOUR GUARANTEE OF QUALITY
AS PUBLISHERS, WE STRIVE TO PRODUCE EVERY BOOK TO THE HIGHEST
COMMERCIAL STANDARDS. THE MUSIC HAS BEEN FRESHLY ENGRAVED AND
THE BOOK HAS BEEN CAREFULLY DESIGNED TO MINIMISE AWKWARD PAGE
TURNS AND TO MAKE PLAYING FROM IT A REAL PLEASURE.
PARTICULAR CARE HAS BEEN GIVEN TO SPECIFYING ACID-FREE, NEUTRAL-
SIZED PAPER MADE FROM PULPS WHICH HAVE NOT BEEN ELEMENTAL
CHLORINE BLEACHED. THIS PULP IS FROM FARMED SUSTAINABLE FORESTS
AND WAS PRODUCED WITH SPECIAL REGARD FOR THE ENVIRONMENT.
THROUGHOUT, THE PRINTING AND BINDING HAVE BEEN PLANNED TO
ENSURE A STURDY, ATTRACTIVE PUBLICATION WHICH SHOULD GIVE YEARS
OF ENJOYMENT. IF YOUR COPY FAILS TO MEET OUR HIGH STANDARDS,
PLEASE INFORM US AND WE WILL GLADLY REPLACE IT.

WWW.MUSICSALES.COM

ONE DIRECTION

Another World

**Words & Music by Nadir Khayat, Bilal Hajji, Geraldo Jacop Sandell,
Achraf Jannusi, Slam Geo & Eric Sanicola**

'Another World' was released as the B-side on One Direction's second single, 'Gotta Be You.' Although the song is yet to appear on a full album by the band, it remains a firm fan favourite online, often mentioned on 1D forums as one of the tracks listeners most want to hear performed live.

Hints & Tips: Make the most of the dynamics in this. Bar 8 is marked *mp* but there's a *crescendo* leading up to the chorus.

Change My Mind

Words & Music by Savan Kotecha, Carl Falk & Rami Yacoub

Louis, who begins the first verse of 'Change My Mind', spent his first paycheck on adopting a chimpanzee called Larry, and admits he's a bit of monkey himself being the messiest member of the band!

Hints & Tips: The fingering in bar 7 is quite tricky. Have your thumb ready to go right under after your third finger has played the F sharp.

Gotta Be You

Words & Music by Steve Mac & August Rigo

'Gotta Be You' was released as One Direction's second single from their smash hit debut album *Up All Night*.
Peaking at number three on both the UK and Irish singles charts, it was 1D's second top ten in both countries.

Hints & Tips: The left hand is just a two-bar pattern repeated all the way through. Once you're comfortable
with the fingering and hand position changes, fitting the right hand in will be easy.

Kiss You

Words & Music by Savan Kotecha, Kristian Lundin, Carl Falk, Rami Yacoub, Shellback, Kristoffer Fogelmark & Albin Nedler

The video for 'Kiss You' features the boys performing their way through a number of classic film and music video scenes including *South Pacific*, Elvis Presley's *Jailhouse Rock*, The Beach Boys' *Surfer Girl* and *Mein Land* by German industrial metal band Rammstein. With 10.4 million views in its first 24 hours of release, it narrowly missed out on Justin Bieber's online video record of 10.6 million views for 'Beauty And A Beat'.

Hints & Tips: There are some difficult rhythms in this, so practise both hands separately and slowly until you've got the hang of them, then practise together.

Last First Kiss

**Words & Music by Savan Kotecha, Carl Falk, Rami Yacoub,
Kristoffer Fogelmark, Albin Nedler, Liam Payne, Zain Malik & Louis Tomlinson**

'Last First Kiss' was co-written by 1D members Liam, Louis and Zayn and a hugely successful songwriting team
made up of Kristoffer Fogelmark, Albin Nedler, Savan Kotecha, Rami Yacoub and Carl Falk. The song is also
alternatively titled 'Last'.

Hints & Tips: In bars 17 and 18, make sure you hold the F in the right hand for the full 3 beats, underneath the
moving melody.

Little Things

Words & Music by Ed Sheeran & Fiona Bevan

Specially written for the band by Ed Sheeran and Fiona Bevan, 'Little Things' was 1D's second UK No. 1 hit single. The song's video is set in the recording studio as the track is being recorded, with Zayn starting to sing as Niall plays guitar before the rest of the band join in.

Hints & Tips: Play this with feeling. The left hand should be smooth and even throughout.

Everything About You

**Words & Music by Wayne Hector, Stephen Robson, Harry Styles,
Niall Horan, Liam Payne, Zain Malik & Louis Tomlinson**

Writing 'Everything About You' for their debut album *Up All Night* was a team effort with all five boys adding in
their ideas to share the writing credits with acclaimed songwriters Steve Robson and Wayne Hector.

Hints & Tips: Don't let the tempo drag or it will become sluggish. Keep it moving, but be careful not to rush!

Live While We're Young

Words & Music by Savan Kotecha, Carl Falk & Rami Yacoub

'Live While We're Young' was a major hit even before it went on general sale, setting the record for being the most pre-ordered song in Sony's history within two days of its release. With its thumping tempo and upbeat sound, the song scored One Direction the number three spot both on the UK and US singles charts.

Hints & Tips: At the start, both hands are playing the same quaver pattern rhythmically but not melodically. Check the notes carefully so you're not caught out.

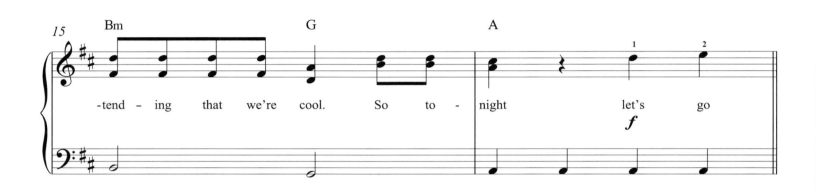

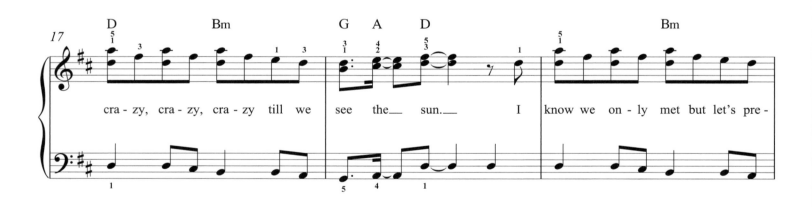

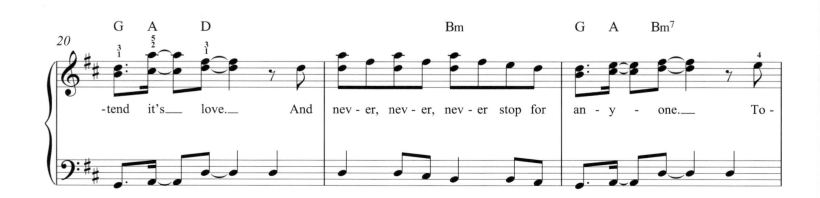

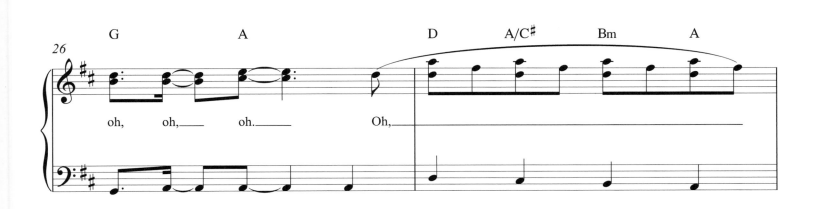

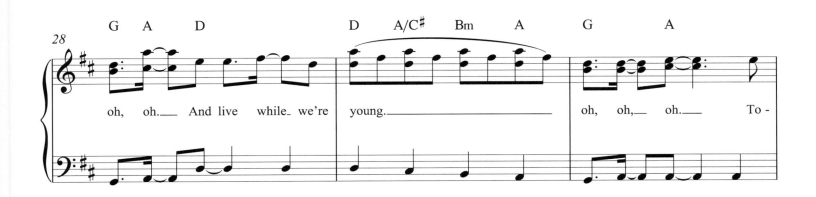

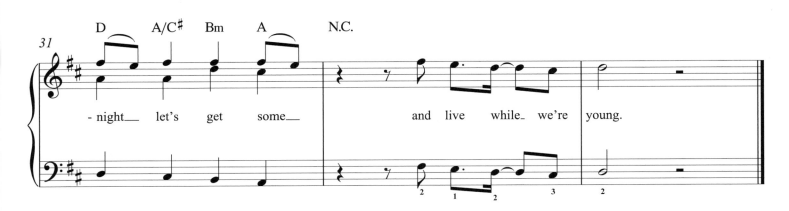

Moments

Words & Music by Ed Sheeran & Simon Hulbert

'Moments' was penned for the band by Ed Sheeran and songwriter Si Hulbert. Sheeran offered the song to One Direction after Harry spoke to the double BRIT winning singer-songwriter about extra material for their debut album, *Up All Night*. The song was included on the set list for the *Up All Night* world tour.

Hints & Tips: While the left hand has same pattern all the way through, the hand position changes. Make sure you know where the changes are so you can get you fingers ready.

More Than This

Words & Music by Jamie Scott

Although best known for their up-tempo pop hits, through tracks such as acoustic ballad 'More Than This'
One Direction have been able to showcase their variety and range of talent. Following the track's release, critics
praised the band for the song's slower, weightier sound.

Hints & Tips: There's a descending left hand pattern at start, so play this through on its own until you get the
hang of the fingering.

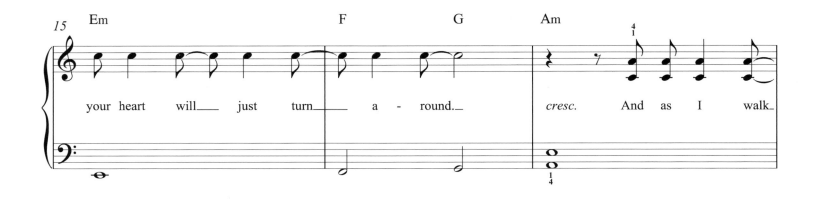

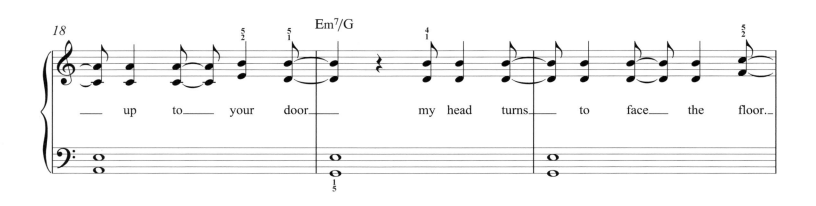

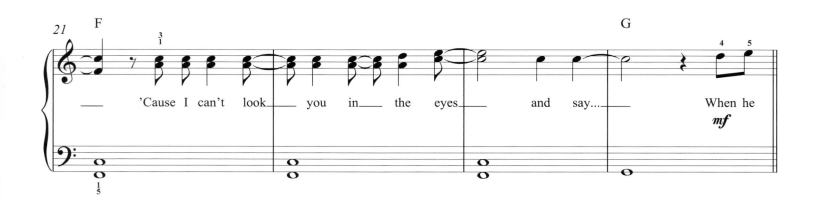

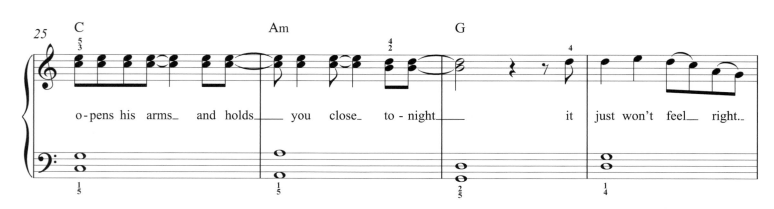

26

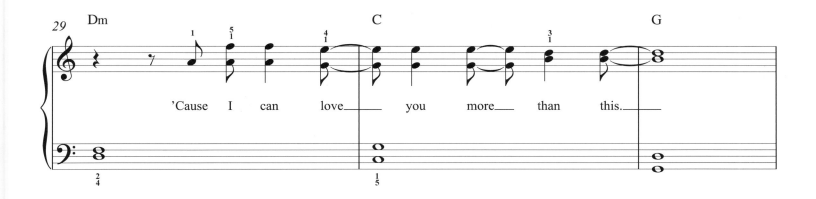

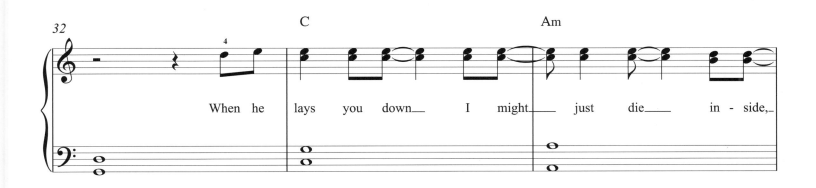

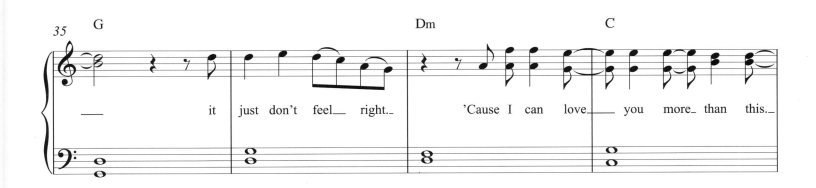

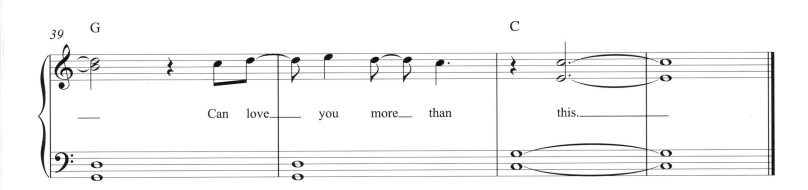

One Thing

Words & Music by Carl Falk, Yami Racoub & Savan Cotecha

With its distorted guitar riffs, anthemic chorus and soaring vocal lines, 'One Thing' is cited by Liam and Niall as their favourite song from the band's debut album, *Up All Night*. The song was a top ten hit in the UK and was One Direction's second US single.

Hints & Tips: Note that each section of this song has a different dynamic marking, starting at *mp* and ending *f*. Make this distinction clear when playing.

29

One Way Or Another (Teenage Kicks)

Words & Music by John O'Neill, Deborah Harry & Nigel Harrison

A medley of Blondie's 'One Way Or Another' and 'Teenage Kicks' by the Undertones, One Direction's 'One Way Or Another (Teenage Kicks)' was released as the official single of Red Nose Day 2013. The song sold 113,000 copies in its first week, helping to raise funds for the Red Nose Day cause.

Hints & Tips: There are accidentals throughout, plus a key change and some chromatic passages- so watch out!

Rock Me

Words & Music by Peter Svensson, Lukasz Gottwald,
Henry Russell Walter, Sam Hollander & Allan Grigg

Harry Styles counts his most recognisable features and habits as his curly hair, dimples, trademark blazer and being flirtatious and cheeky. Don't approach Harry with any goats or snakes however, he's terrified of them! As well as being a member of One Direction and a modern-day pop icon, Harry is also a fan of knitting and a skilled kazoo player.

Hints & Tips: Practise the right hand of bars 21–22 on it's own until you're confident with it.

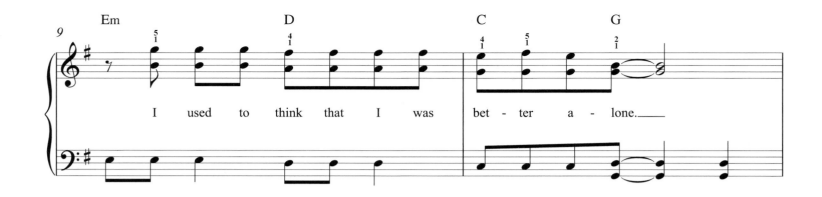

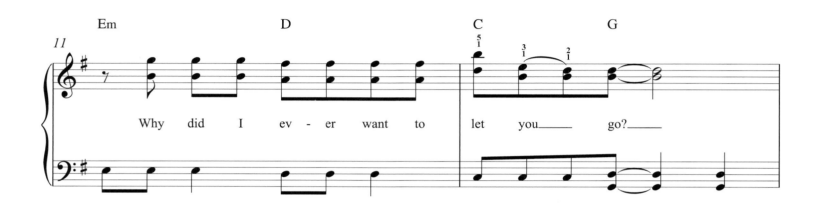

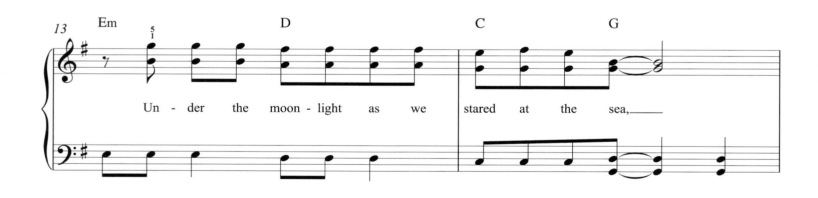

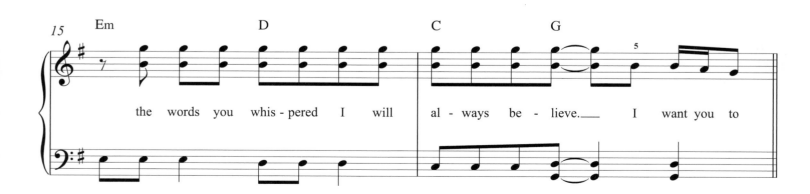

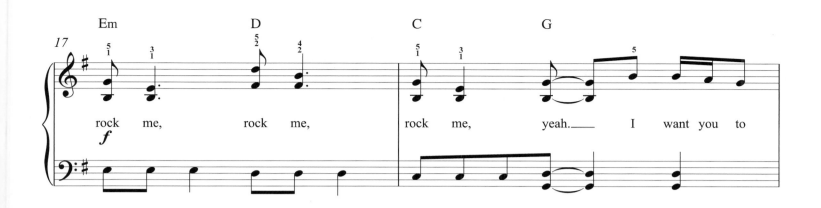

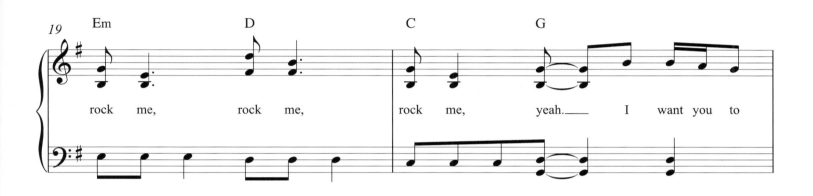

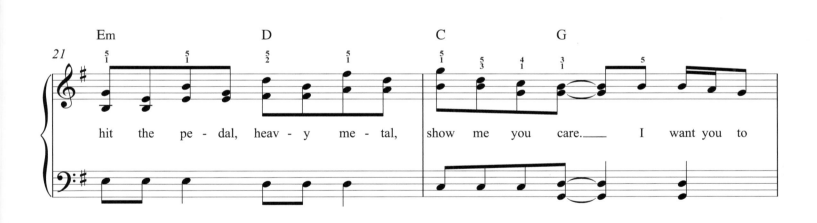

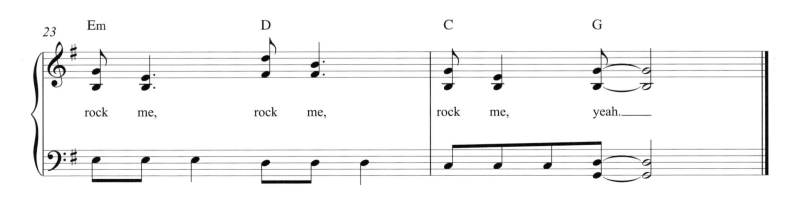

Summer Love

Words & Music by Wayne Hector, Guy Chambers, Stephen Robson, Lindy Robbins, Niall Horan, Liam Payne, Zain Malik & Louis Tomlinson

As well as leading the chorus to 'Summer Love', Niall Horan is One Direction's Irish connection, born in Mullingar, Ireland. His signature blonde hair is in fact dyed, as Niall's natural hair colour is brown. Although unable to play the piano, he is a keen guitarist, citing his guitar as the best Christmas present he has ever received.

Hints & Tips: Look out for the E flat accidentals that crop up in the second half. Play the passages with slurs nice and smoothly.

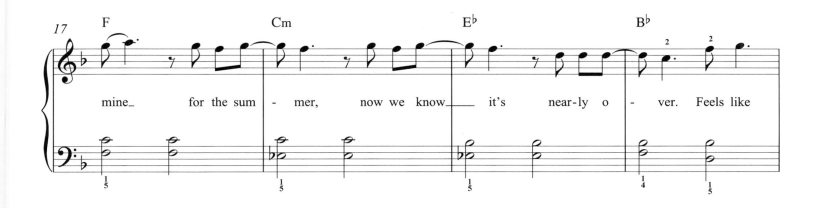

mine___ for the sum - mer, now we know___ it's near-ly o - ver. Feels like

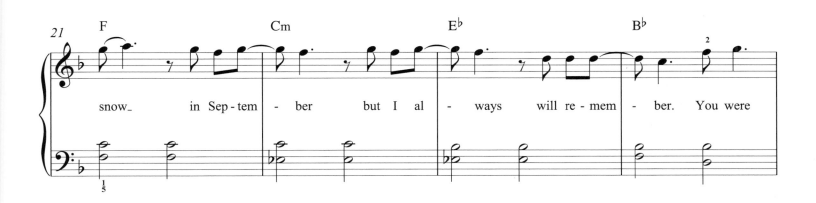

snow___ in Sep-tem - ber but I al - ways will re - mem - ber. You were

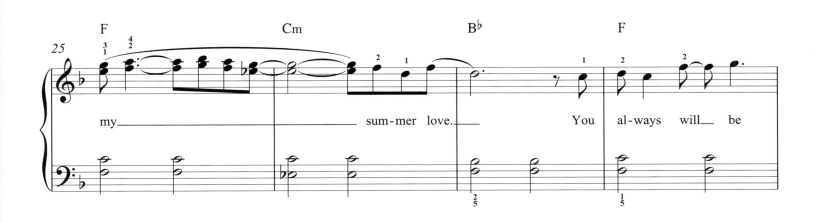

my_____ sum-mer love.___ You al-ways will___ be

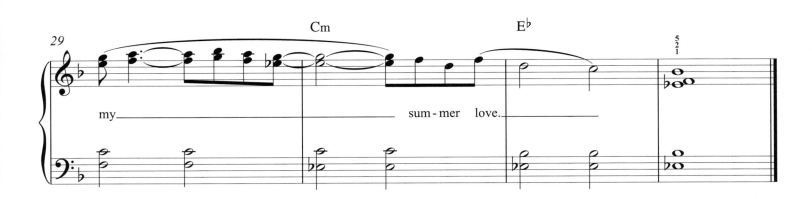

my_____ sum-mer love.___

Taken

**Words & Music by Lindy Robbins, Tobias Gad, Harry Styles,
Niall Horan, Liam Payne, Zain Malik & Louis Tomlinson**

Liam is said to be the most competitive member of the band. He studied Music Technology at college and first entered The X Factor in 2008 aged just 14. After the age limit for entry was raised to 16, he was made to wait before he had the chance to try again, when he signed up for the 2010 series, eventually becoming a member of One Direction.

Hints & Tips: There are a lot of thirds in the right hand. Be sure to bring your fingers down on the keys at the same time, so the notes sound exactly together.

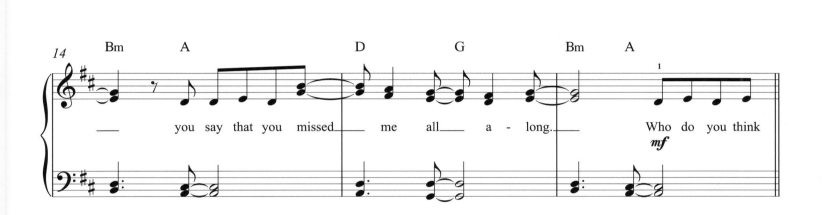

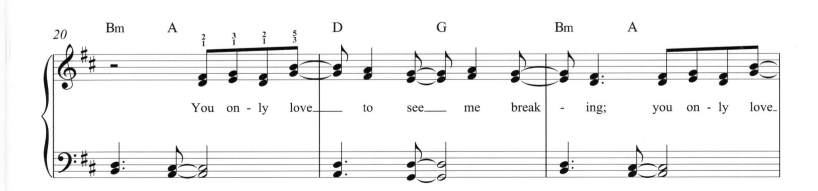

39

Tell Me A Lie

Words & Music by Sheppard Solomon, Kelly Clarkson
& Thomas Meredith

'Tell Me A Lie' was written for One Direction's debut album *Up All Night* by US singer-songwriter Kelly Clarkson and songwriters Tom Meredith and Shep Soloman. Clarkson originally created the track to be included in her own album *Stronger*, but after it was leaked she decided to give the song to One Direction.

Hints & Tips: Keep the chords in the left hand steady. Play through slowly at first and work up to full speed.

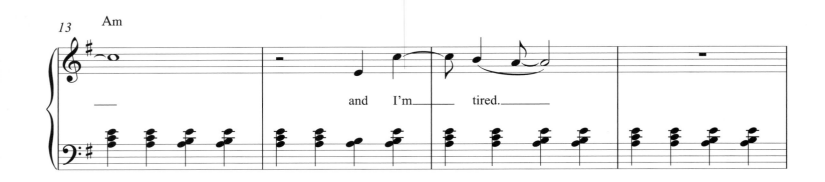

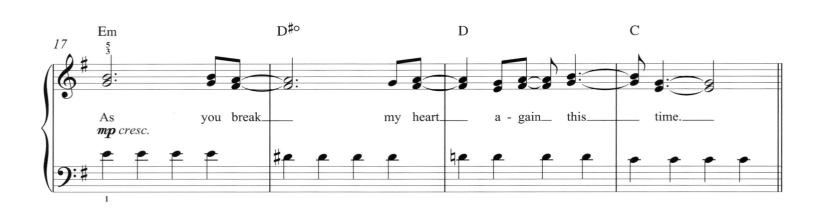

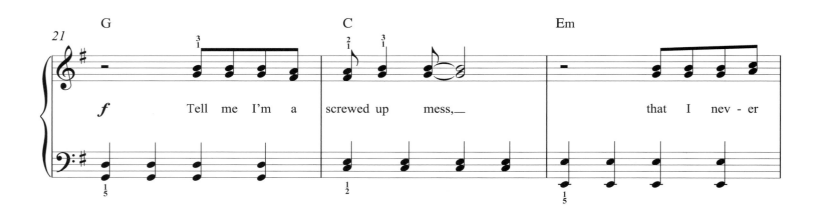

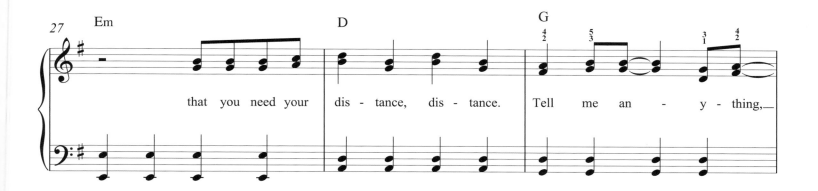

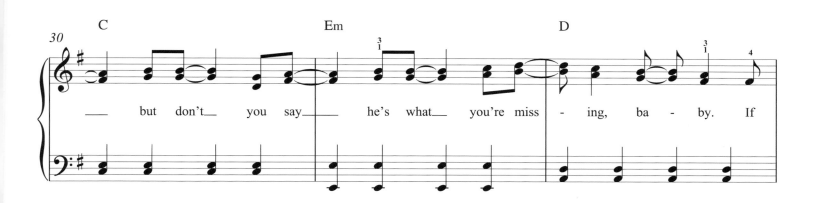

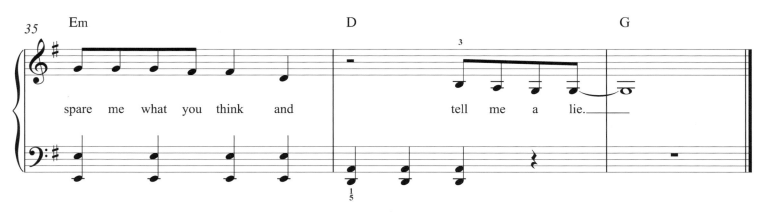

They Don't Know About Us

Words & Music by Tommy James, Peter Wallevik,
Tebey Ottoh & Tommy Gregersen

Early on in the process of creating their second album, the group stated that they wanted to contribute more to the song writing. Written in collaboration between Harry, Louis and songwriters Tebey Ottoh, Tommy Lee James, Peter Wallevik and Tommy P Gregersen, this song is one of the many tracks from *Take Me Home* to feature members of the band on the writing credits.

Hints & Tips: Count carefully, as the left hand notes are often tied over to the next bar.

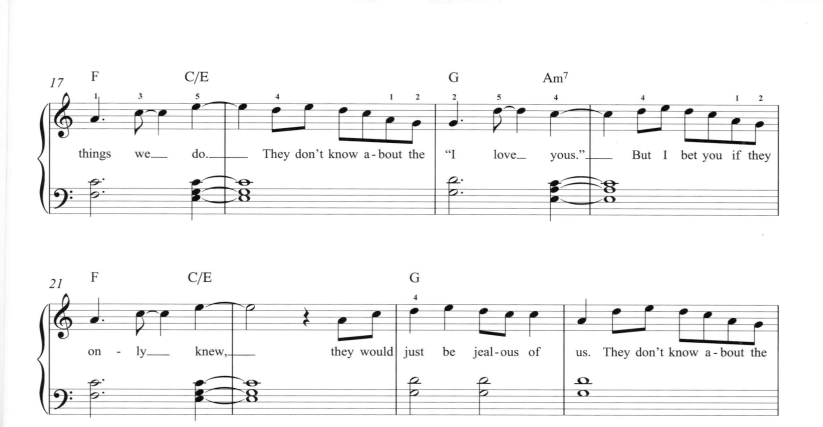

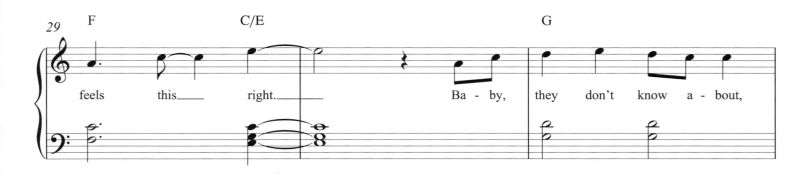

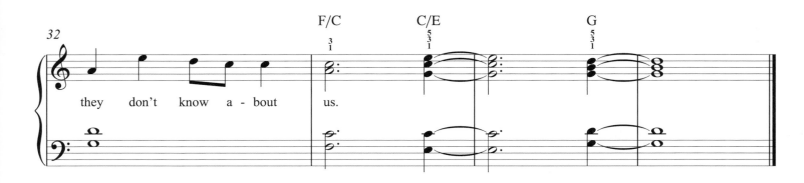

What Makes You Beautiful

Words & Music by Savan Kotecha, Carl Falk & Rami Yacoub

The success of this song helped to propel One Direction into becoming one of the biggest pop acts around, conquering the USA and the head of a new British Invasion. At the 2012 BRIT Awards the band's success was recognised with the trophy for Best British Single, an award that was soon joined by gongs from the MTV Video Music Awards and Teen Choice Awards.

Hints & Tips: Don't be tempted to hold down the left hand notes too long; the rests should be given the full count.

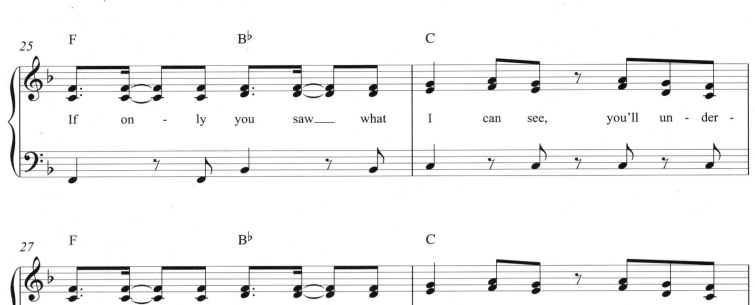

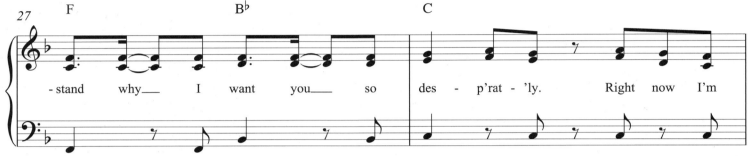

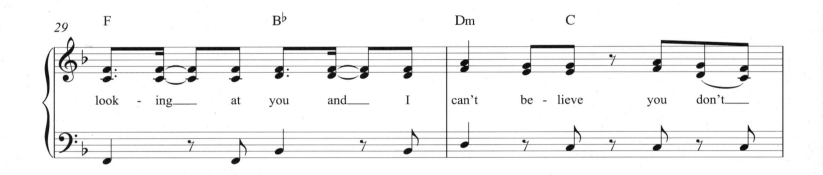

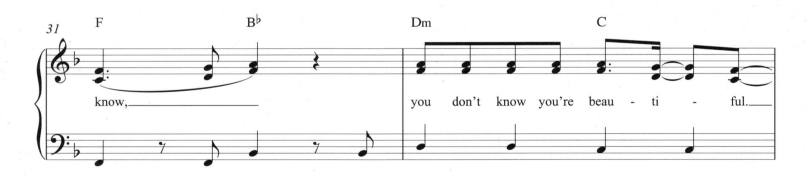